CREATIVE COLOURING
FOR GROWN-UPS

THE CLASSIC COMIC COLOURING BOOK

Michael O'Mara Books Limited

First published in Great Britain in 2015 by
Michael O'Mara Books Limited
9 Lion Yard
Tremadoc Road
London SW4 7NQ

A CIP catalogue record for this book is available from the British Library.

Papers used by Michael O'Mara Books Limited are natural, recyclable products
made from wood grown in sustainable forests. The manufacturing processes
conform to the environmental regulations of the country of origin.

We have made our best efforts to ensure that the artworks reproduced herein are
all in the public domain. We apologize for any errors, which will be corrected in
future editions.

ISBN: 978-1-78243-409-2

1 2 3 4 5 6 7 8 9 10

www.mombooks.com

Designed by Claire Cater

Printed and bound in China

BLUE BOLT

10¢

August

VOL. 1—NO. 3

SUB-ZERO MAN, SERGEANT SPOOK, SUPERHORSE, PHANTOM SUB, DICK COLE, RUNAWAY RONSON.

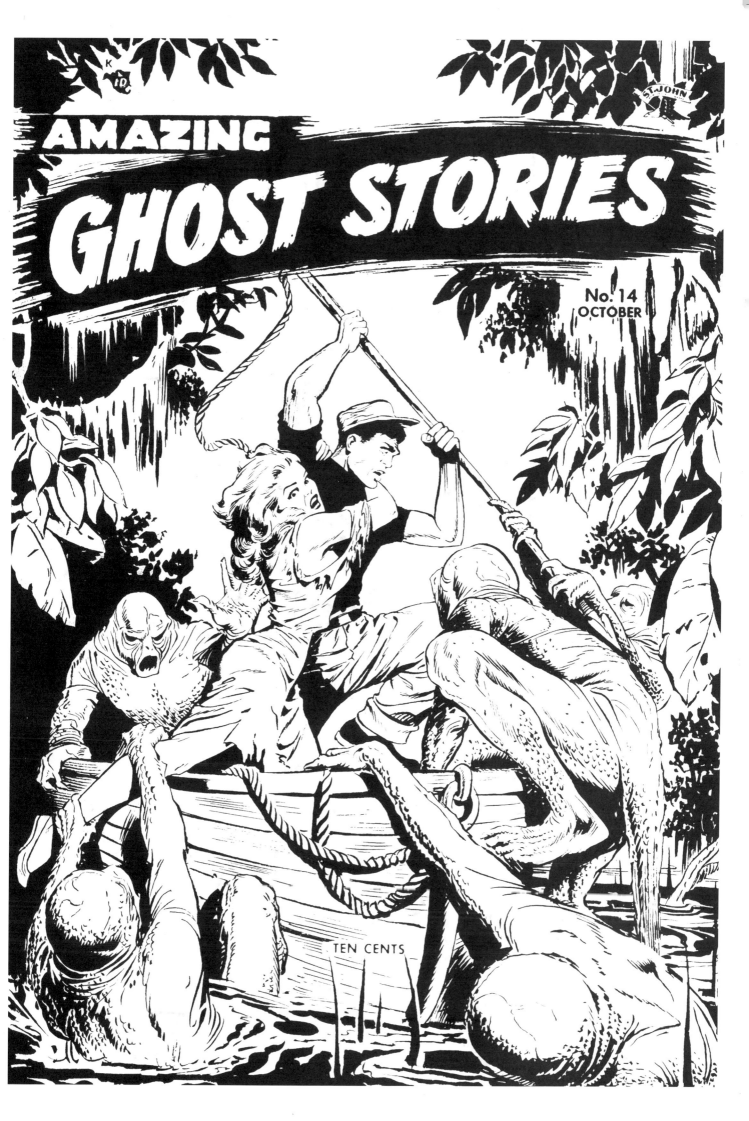

ALL ORIGINAL!!! ALL NEW!!! ALL COMPLETE!!!
BRENDA STARR
NO. 9
JULY
SUPERIOR COMIC
1949
10¢
AUTHORIZED A. C. M. P.
CONFORMS to the COMICS CODE

ALL ORIGINAL!!! ALL NEW!!! ALL COMPLETE!!!
No. 5
APRIL
SUPERIOR COMIC
ANC
BRUCE GENTRY
10c

DETECTIVE EYE

No. 2 DEC. 10c
(15c in Canada)

JACK BARRISTER
with the help of
THE EYE
fights a fierce
BATTLE
on the Ocean floor

•

The **AIRMAN**,
with wings spread,
And ROCKET
BLASTING,
escapes
a fate
Worse Than
DEATH

•

Also —

**Don Rance and
the MYSTICAPE**

•

Ken TRAYMORE

•

PACK MORGAN

•

*10 Exciting
Features*

FDC

DON FORTUNE

AGAZINE

DEC.
No. 5

10¢

DELECTA OF THE PLANETS! DON FORTUNE in THRILL-PACKED ACTION! LOTS OF LAUGH FEATURES!

BAFFLING

WEIRD! FANTASTIC! ASTOUNDING!

JULY

MYSTERIES

10c   No.21

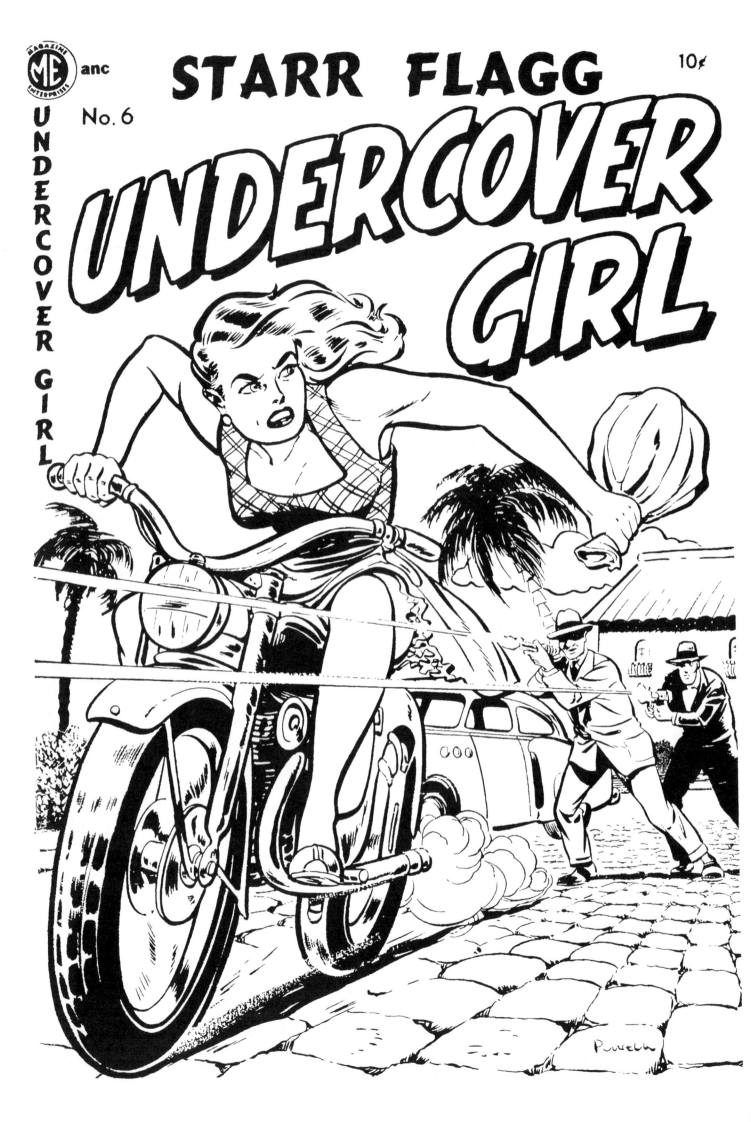

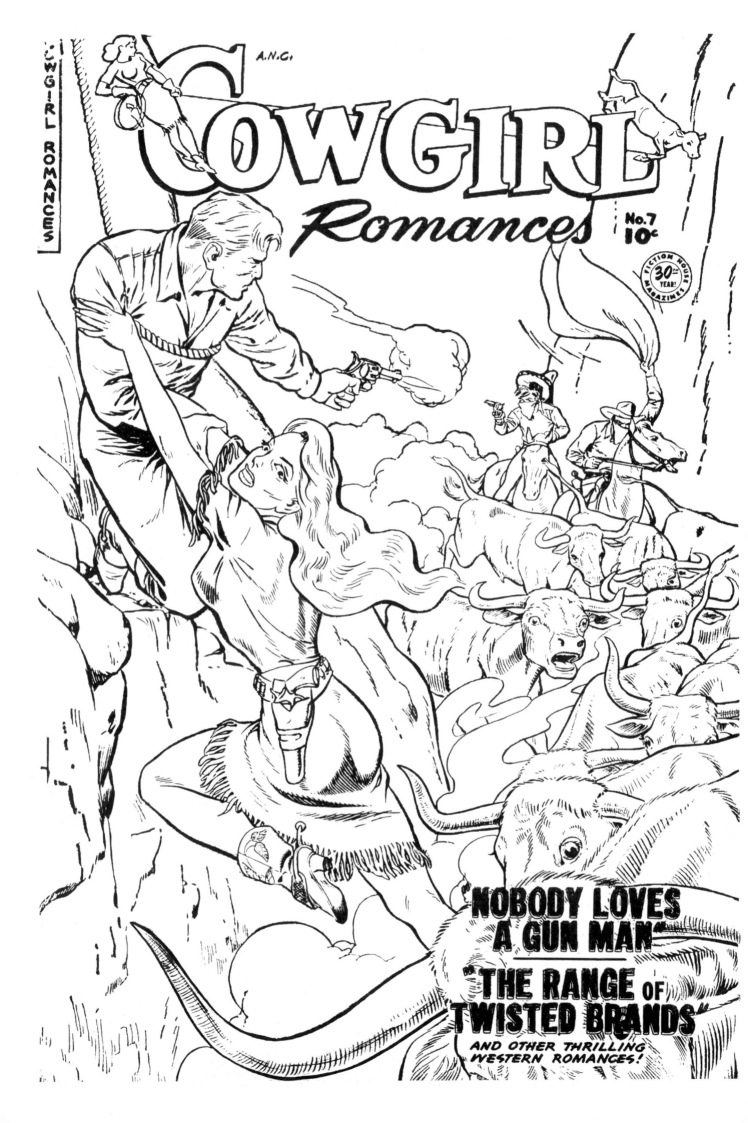

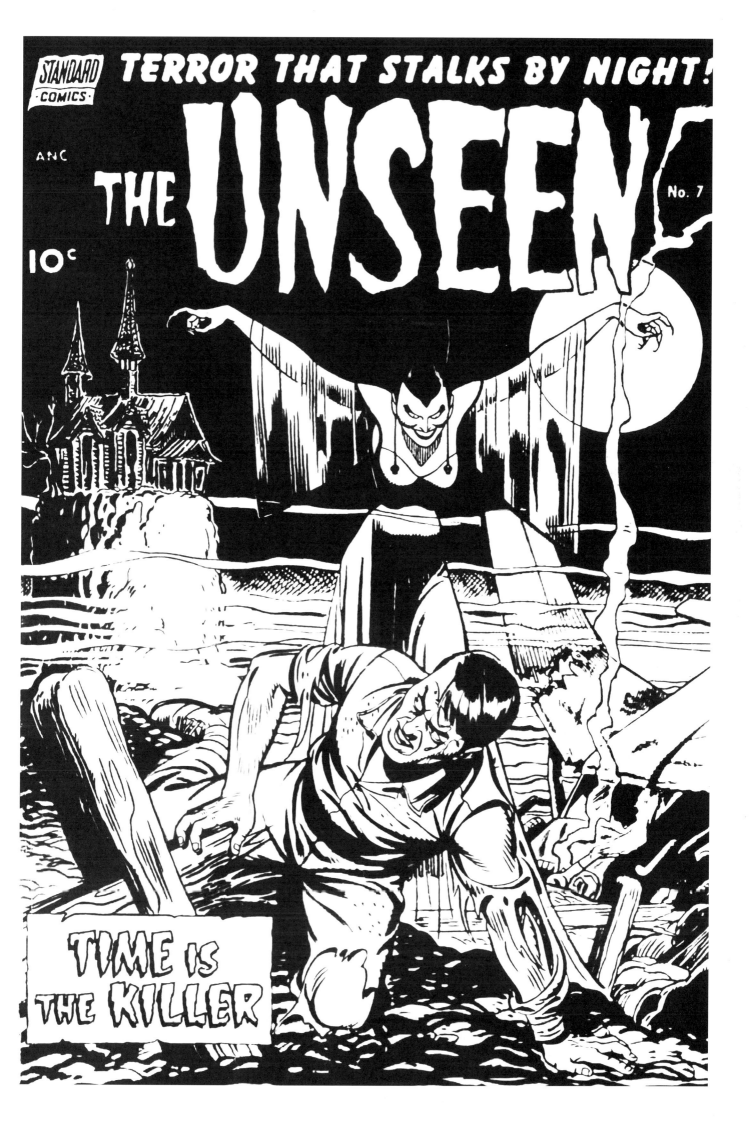

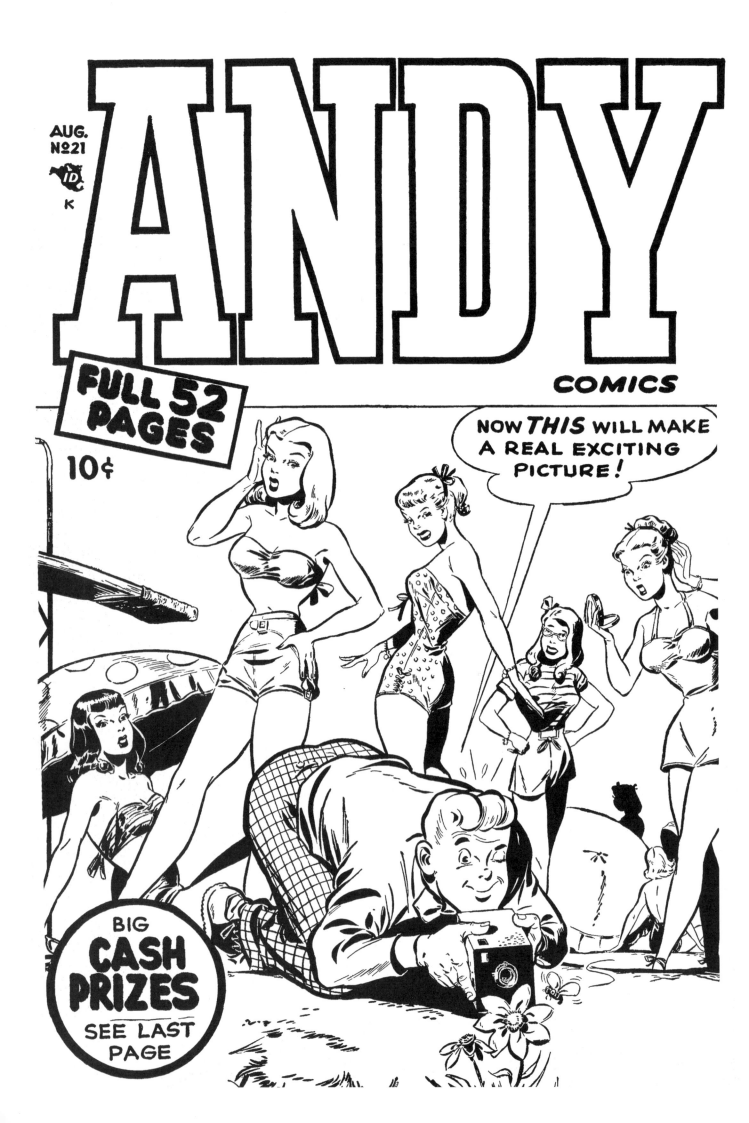

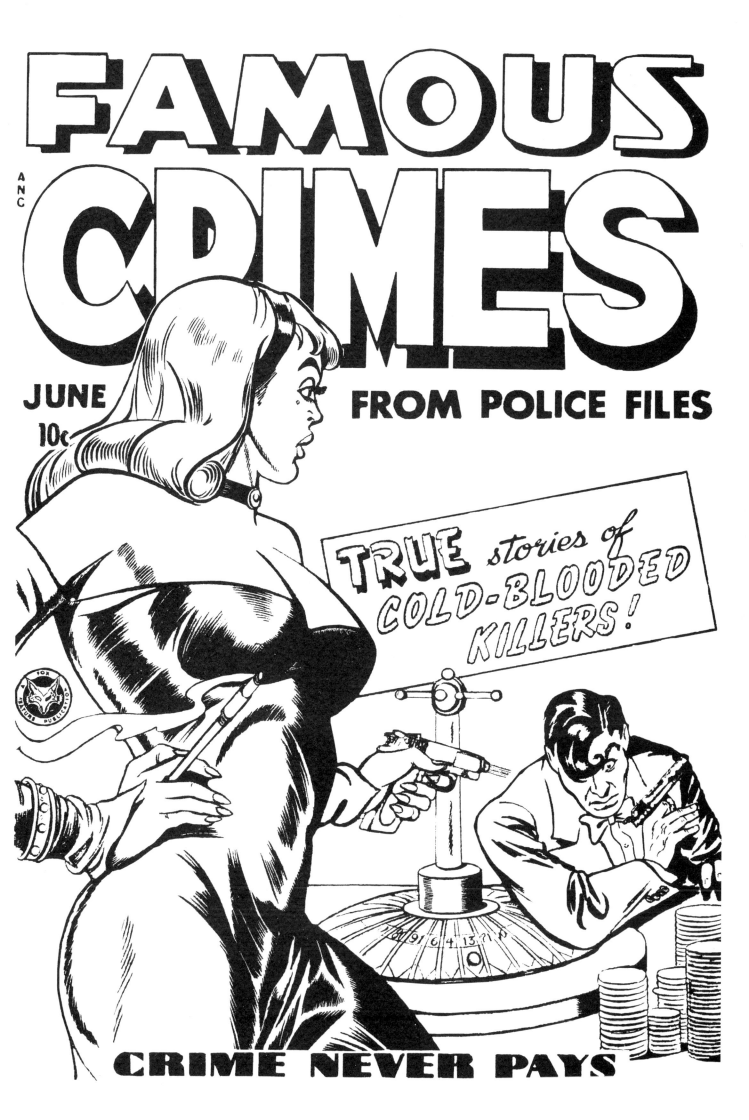

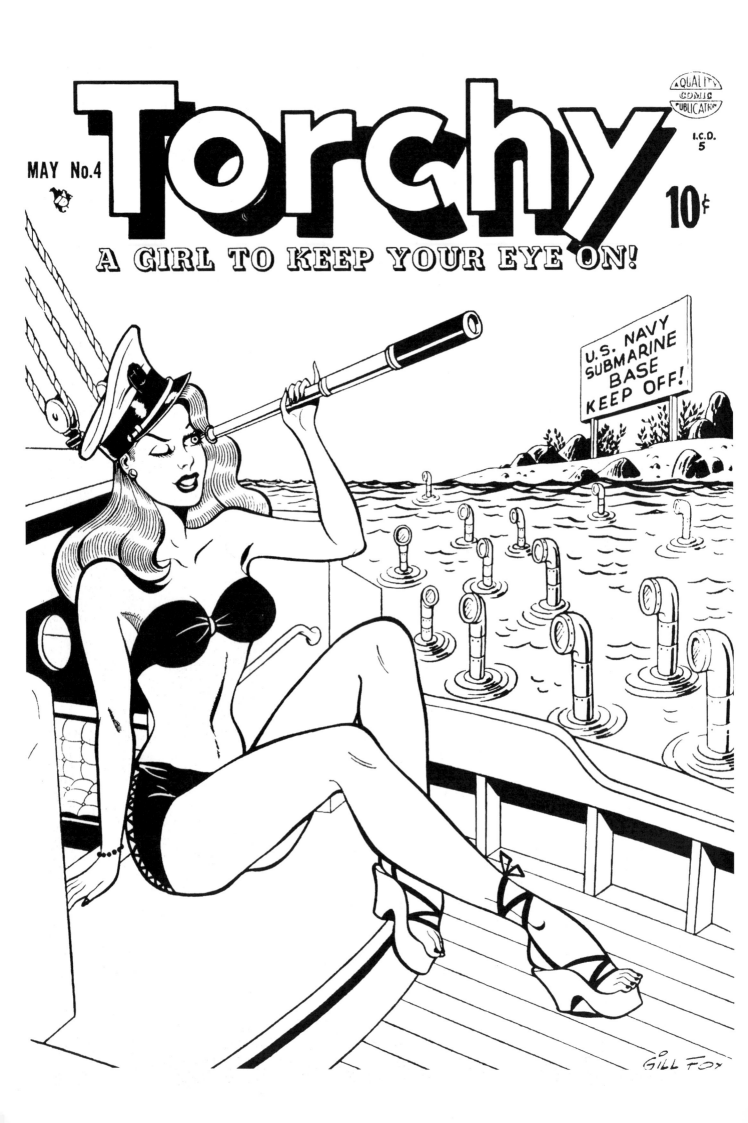

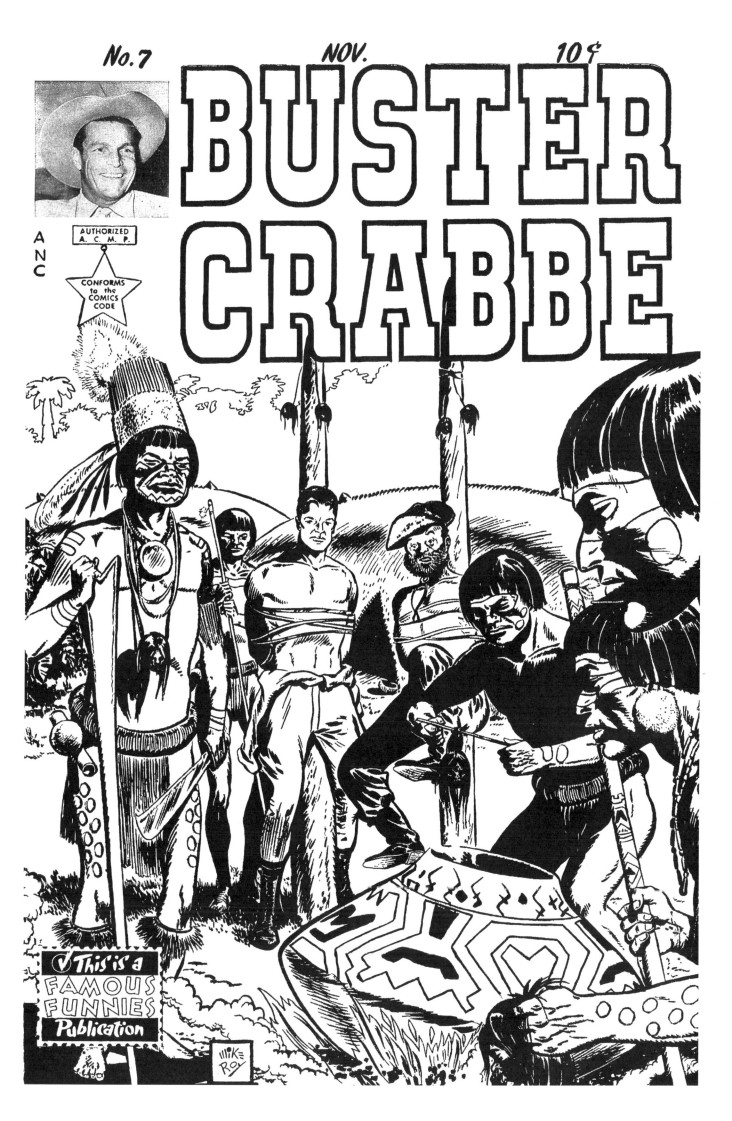

A.N.C.
GHOST COMICS
GHOST
No. 3
10c
COMICS
FICTION HOUSE MAGAZINES
"THE HAUNTED HAND OF X"
"DARK EYES OF DESTINY"
"MISTRESS OF THE WEB"
"I SEEK THE DEVIL-MASK"
ALL IN THIS ISSUE!

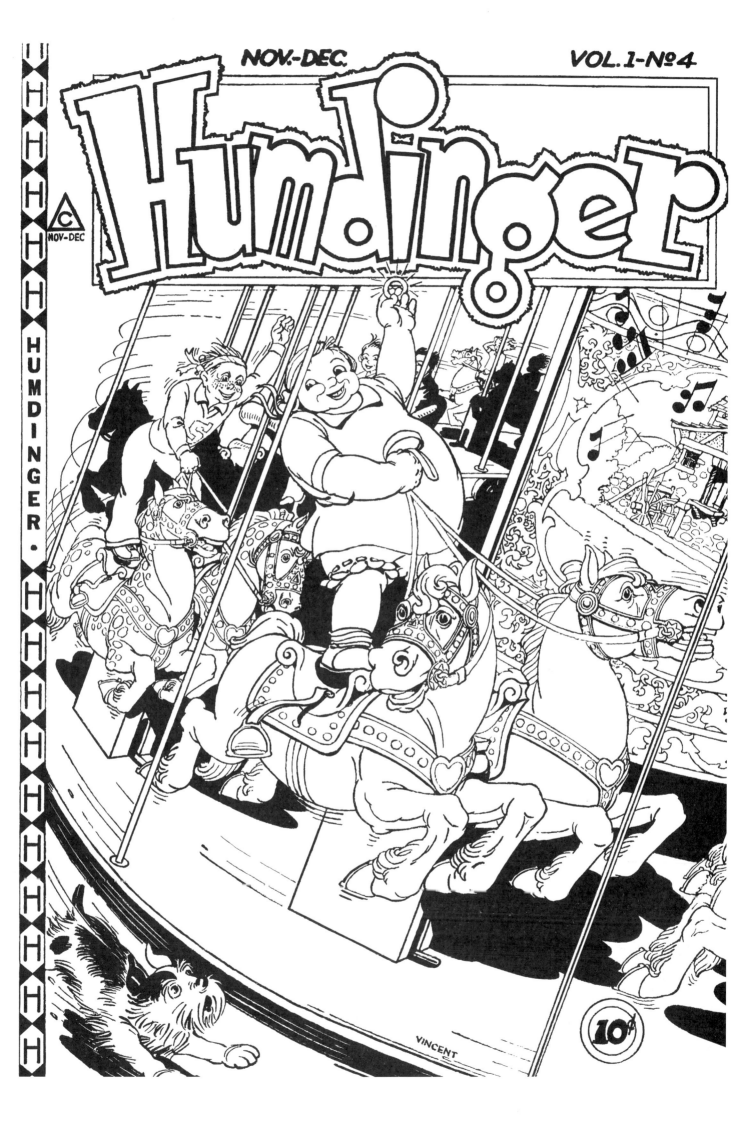

A.N.C.
JUMBO COMICS
No. 118
DEC.
10¢
SHEENA,
QUEEN OF THE JUNGLE, in
"QUEST OF THE CONGO DWARFLINGS!"
GHOST GALLERY
AND MANY OTHERS -
FICTION HOUSE MAGAZINES
52 Pages

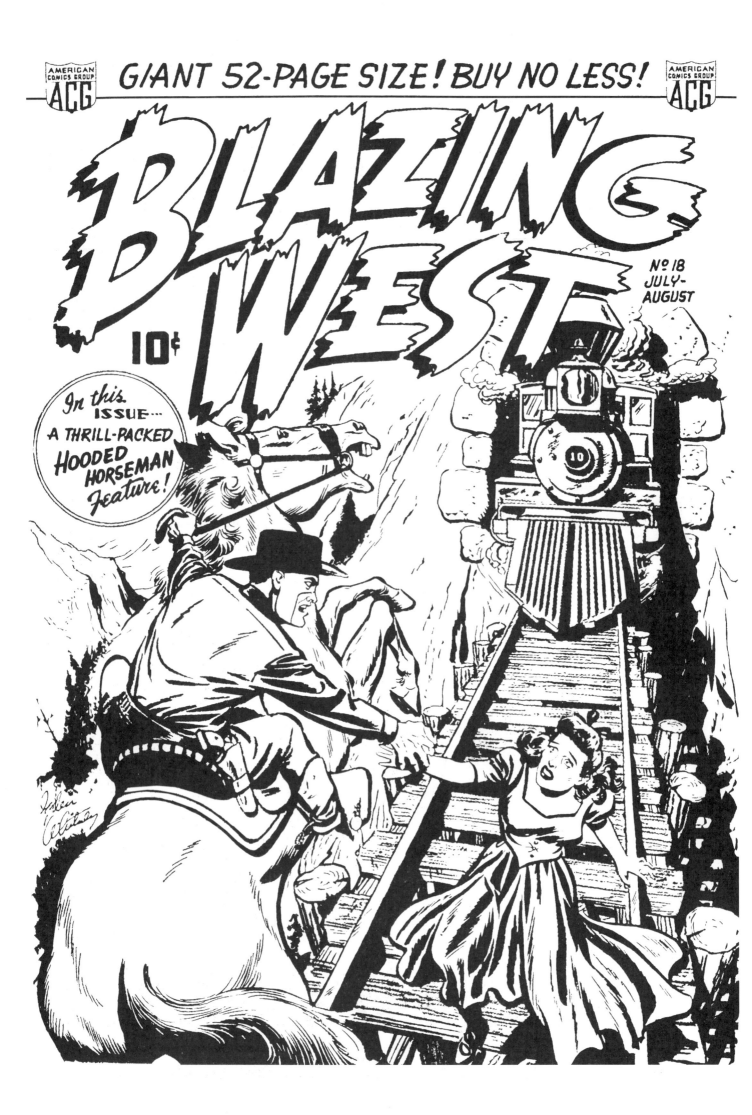

Featuring America's Fighting Nemesis of Crime

10¢

The BLACK TERROR

NO. 13

SLOW CHILDREN

50·50

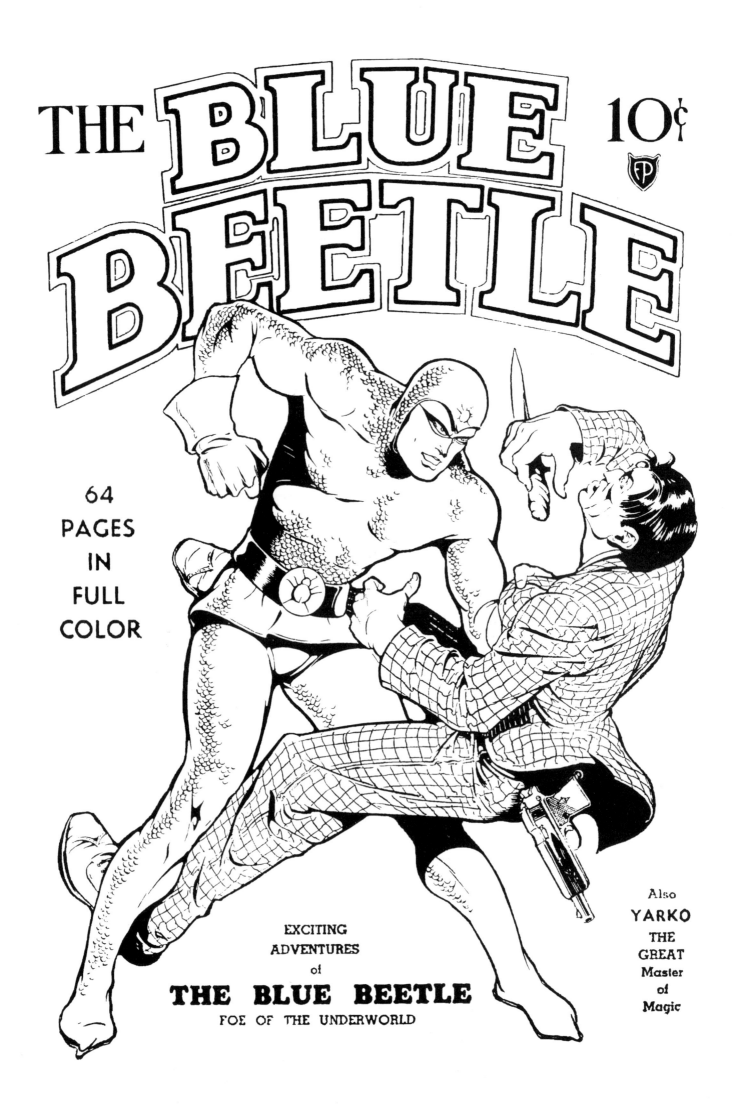

TALES of HORROR and TERROR!

HAUNTED

HAUNTED THRILLS

NOV

10c
K

A Farrell Publication

BULLETMAN.
THE FLYING DETECTIVE

No. II JAN. 13

A FAWCETT PUBLICATION
10c

BULLETMAN BATTLES THE FIENDISH FIDDLER

68 THRILL-PACKED PAGES

COW PUNCHER

AN *Avon* COMIC

10¢

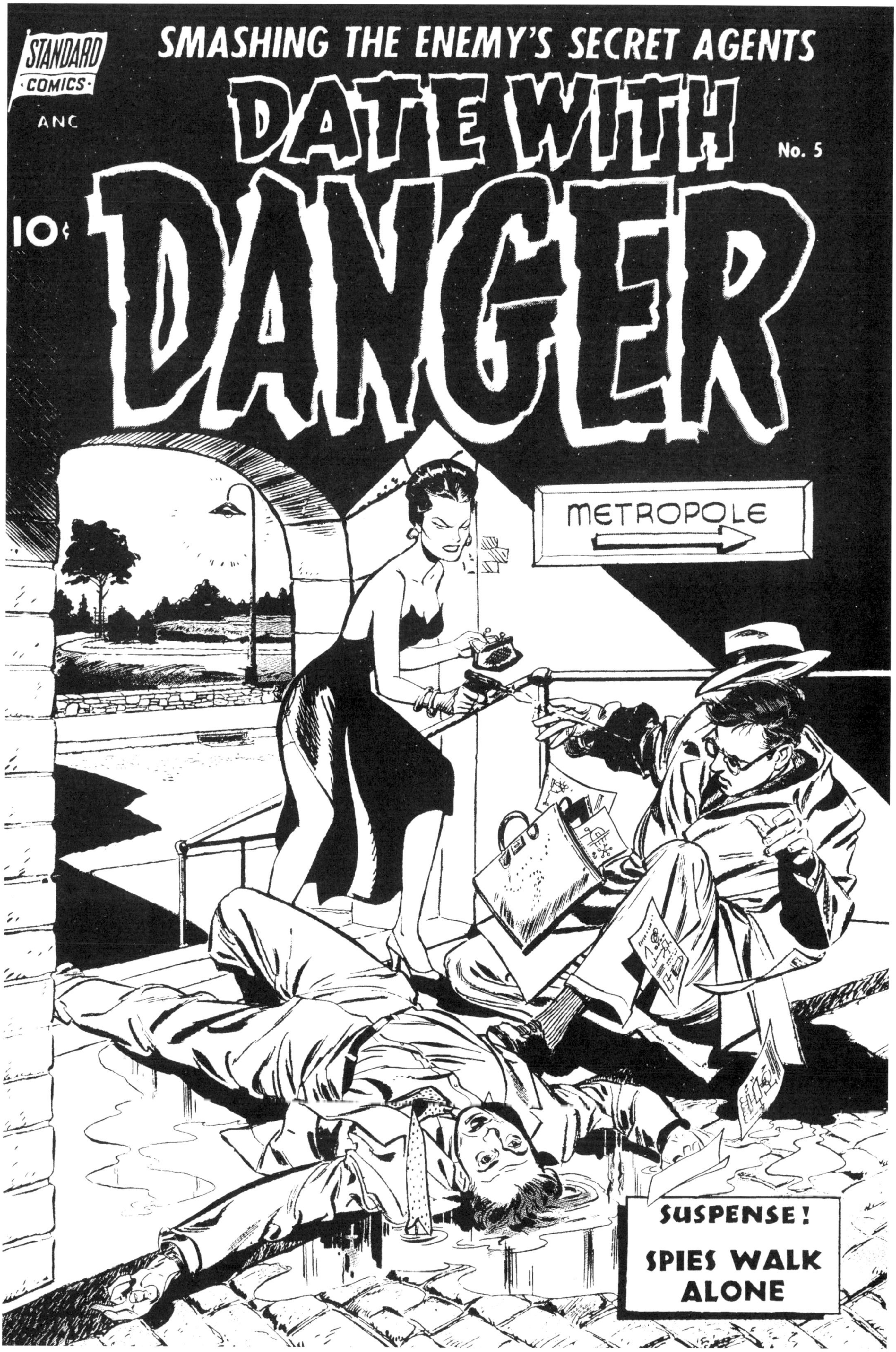
STANDARD COMICS
ANC
SMASHING THE ENEMY'S SECRET AGENTS
DATE WITH DANGER
No. 5
10¢
METROPOLE
SUSPENSE!
SPIES WALK ALONE

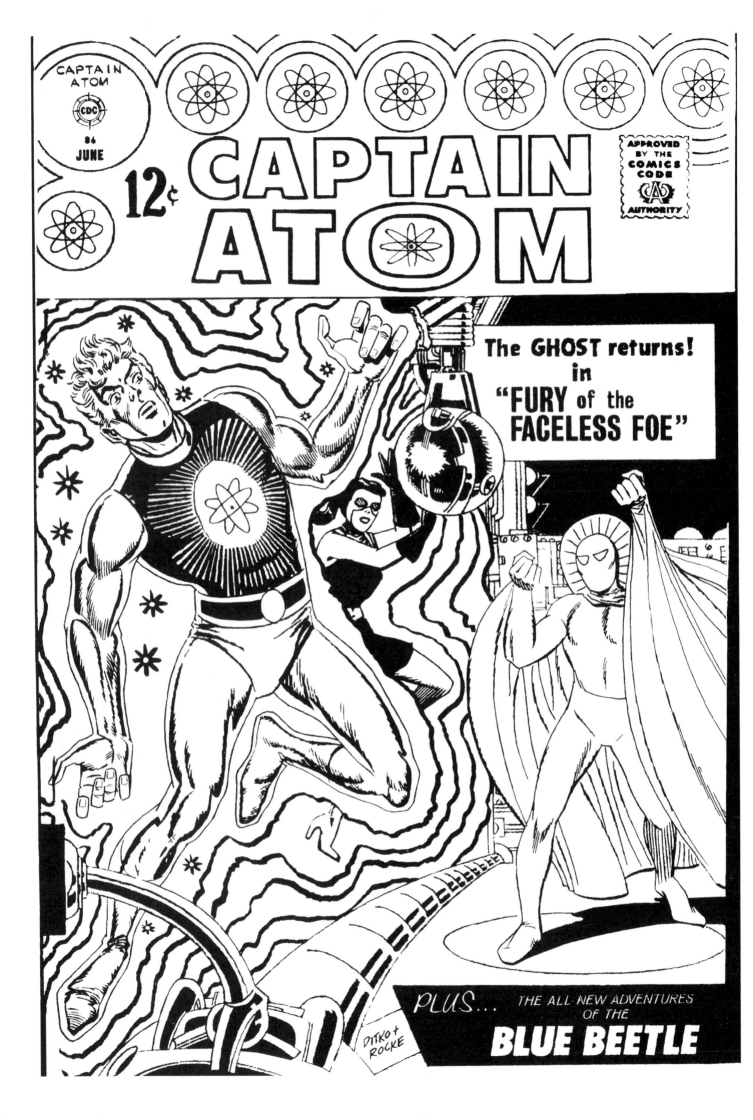

CAT-MAN
COMICS

NO. 1

"America's Most Thrilling, Fast-Action Adventure Stories!"

MAY

10¢

IN THIS ISSUE..
The Sensational
"CAT-MAN"
··
The "DEACON"
A NEW & AMAZING CHARACTER

"HURRICANE" HARRIGAN
A COWBOY IN INDIA!

DR. DIAMOND
MAN OF MYSTERY

"BLAZE" BAYLOR
AND THE ARSON RING

The RAG-MAN ⚡ BLACK WIDOW
HE'S DIFFERENT! ⚡ MURDER IN THE NIGHT

And other great Action Features!

CHAS. M. QUINLAN

UNUSUAL INTERPLANETARY ADVENTURES
ACE
SPACE
ACTION
JUNE
10c
SPACE ACTION
INVADERS FROM
A LOST GALAXY
DOUBLE MENACE
ON JUPITER'S MOON
and other terrific tales

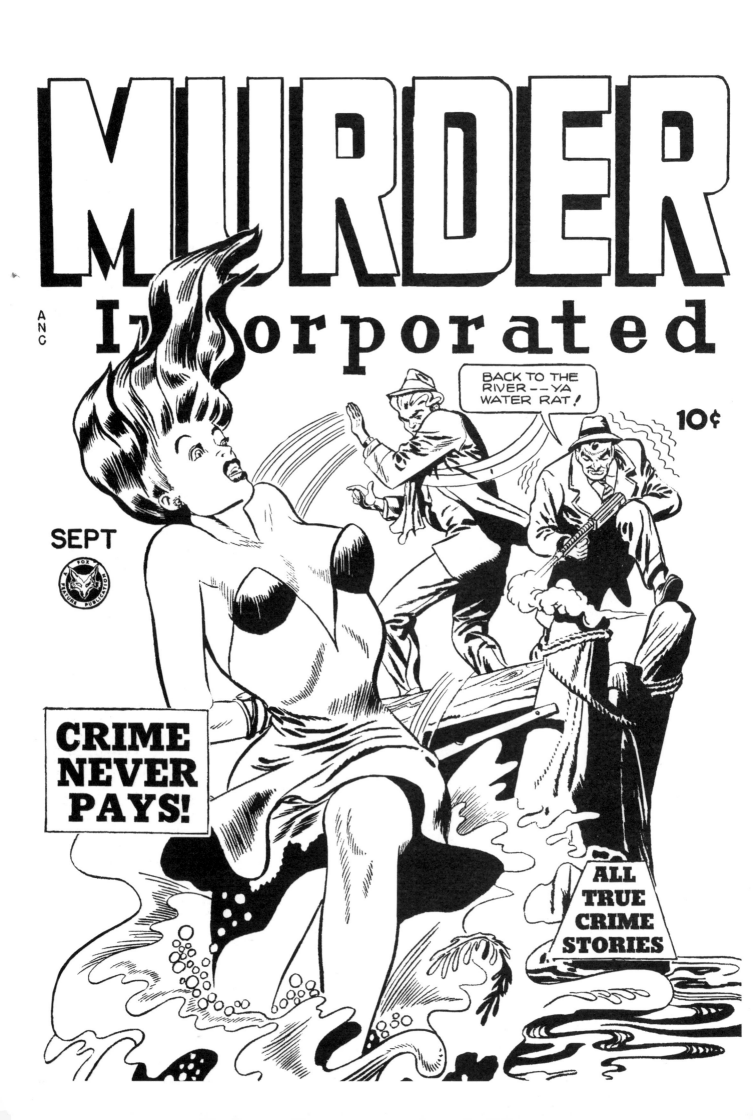

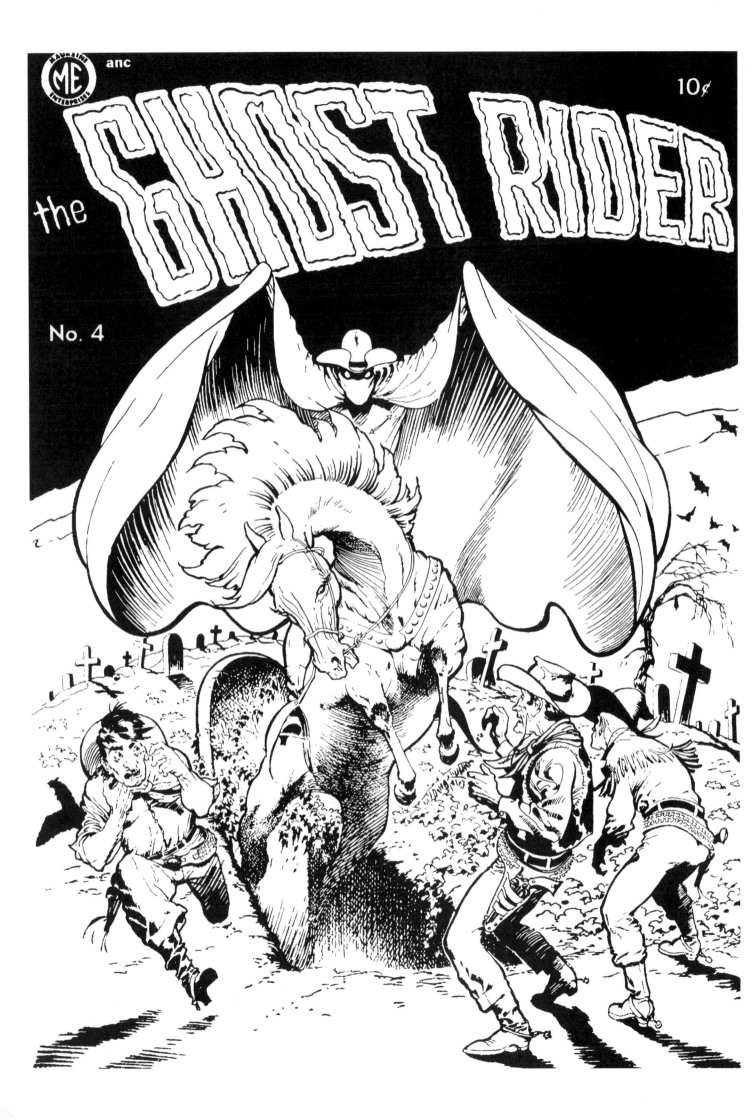

ALL NEW STORIES OF WEIRD TERRORS
A.N.C. No.2 10¢
THE MONSTER
THE MONSTER
FICTION HOUSE MAGAZINES
OUT OF THE ANCIENT OOZE IT CRAWLED—
"THE DARK ABYSMAL"
CW
"THE TIGER KISS"
"KOHNOORI'S CURSE"

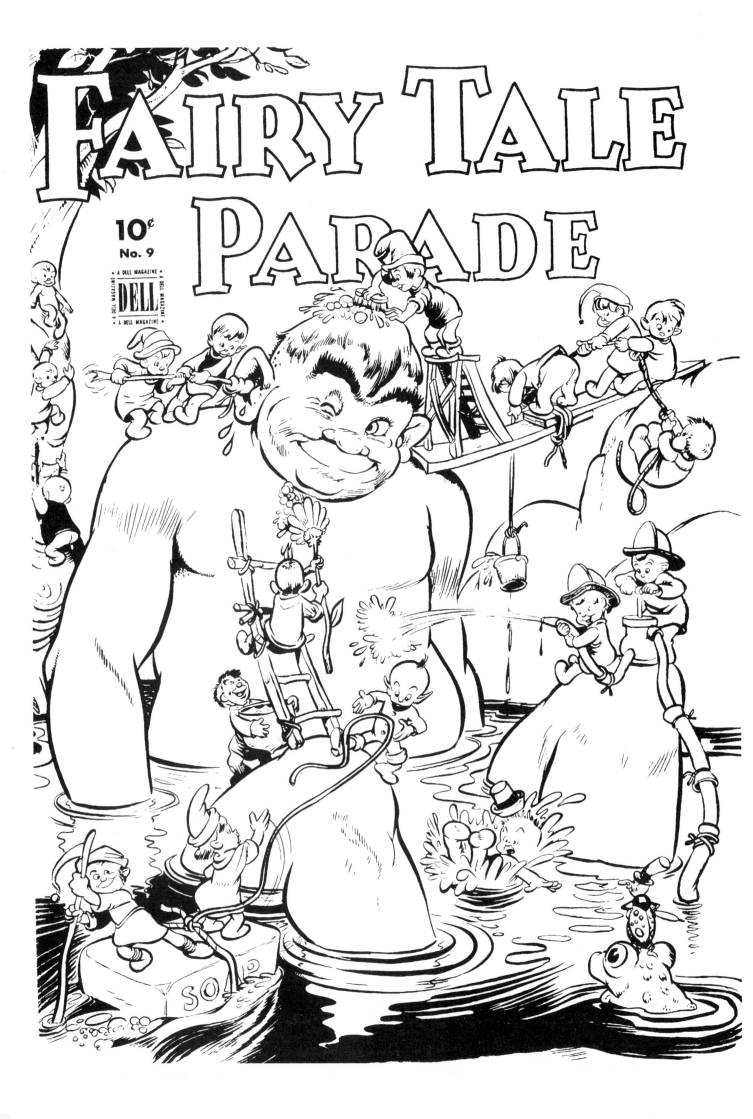

MARCH No 33 ANC

10c

T-MAN

WORLD WIDE TROUBLE-SHOOTER

A QUALITY COMIC PUBLICATION

THE RED MERMAID

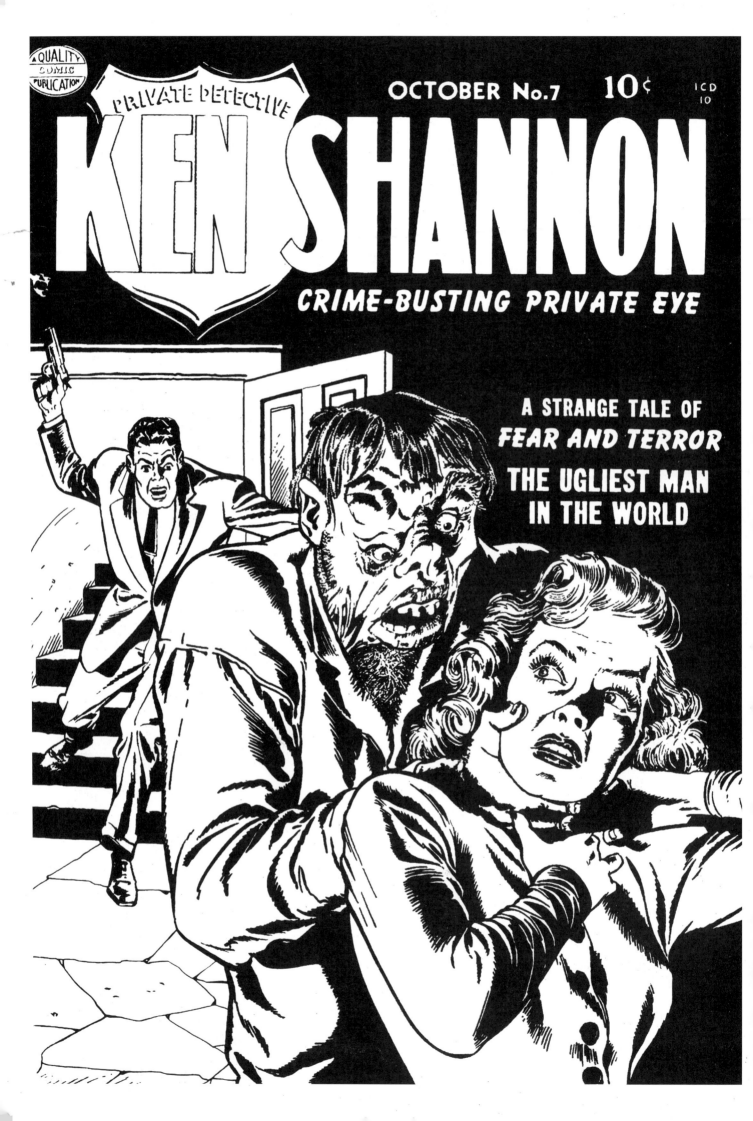

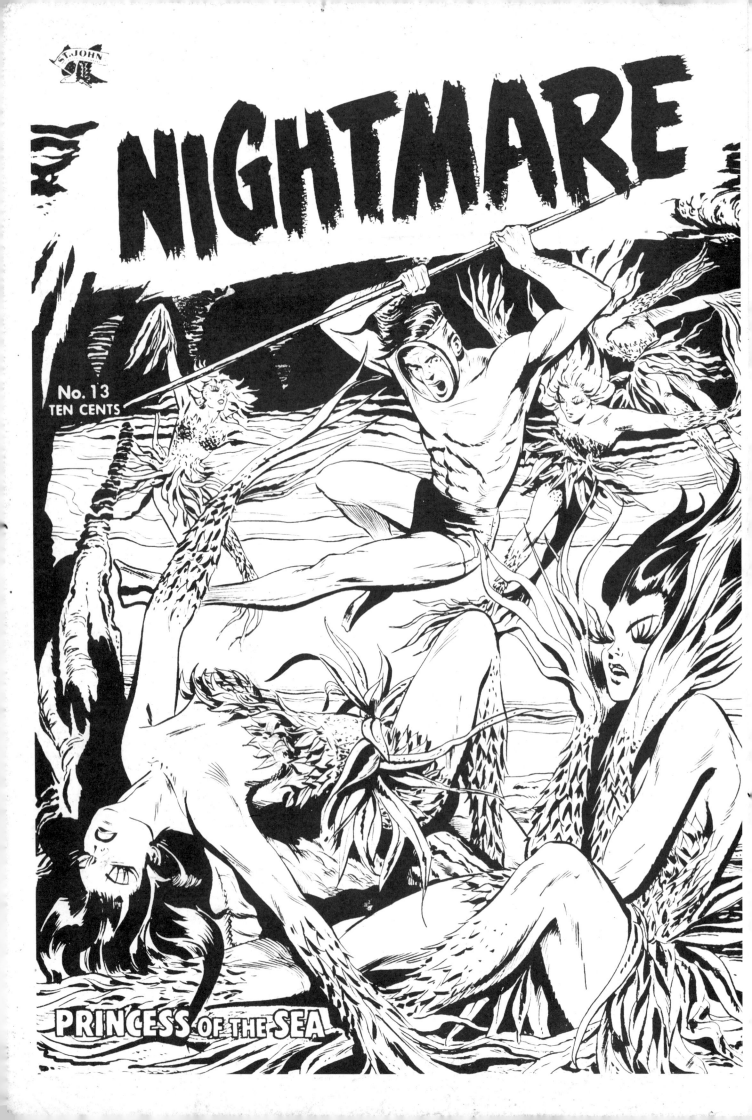